RAIN IN THE WOODS

and Other Small Matters

Rain

Cleveland and New York

GLEN ROUNDS

in the Woods

AND OTHER SMALL MATTERS

The World Publishing Company

Published by The World Publishing Company
2231 West 110th Street, Cleveland 2, Ohio
Published simultaneously in Canada by
Nelson, Foster & Scott Ltd.
Library of Congress Catalog Card Number: 64-12360
FIRST EDITION
COWP

Designed by Jack Jaget

Contents

Anyone Can Have a Private Wildlife Preserve

AN OLD long-abandoned millpond, a stagnant pool in a roadside ditch, and a short stretch of sunken woods road—these are my private wildlife preserves. But almost any neglected bit of weed-grown ground would serve as well. The creatures in these places come in small sizes, as a general thing, but each is as wild as any lion or elephant, and besides, has the advantage of being close at hand.

A battle between a pack of hungry timber wolves and a caribou is a thing not many people ever expect to see, except in motion pictures. But the tiny ants swarming over and around a hairy white caterpillar, here on a sun-baked path, are as savage and bloodthirsty as the wolves could ever be—and the caterpillar at bay fights as stubbornly as the antlered bull. And there is really little to choose—as far as slam-bang action goes—between a lion making his kill and the small wasp's deadly attack on a spider several times her size. It simply depends on the point of view.

7

One reason so many kinds of wildlife manage to carry on their affairs almost underfoot without anyone's suspecting their presence is that most people really pay very little attention to what goes on around them. Anyone who sees well enough to read a newspaper or to recognize a friend across the street can build a reputation for having an eagle eye simply by learning to notice anything out of the ordinary. The patience to stand or sit motionless for what at times may seem endless minutes is a help, also.

Every creature, no matter how small or wild, leaves some trace of its comings and goings. Tiny piles of dirt in the most unlikely places tell of burrowers at work. Squirrels and woodpeckers wear away the weathered outer surface of the bark of their favorite trees, leaving faint paths or patches of a slightly different color. And every spot of soft sand or wet dirt holds footprints of the latest travelers.

Another reason for their apparent invisibility is that most wild things live and work close to the ground, below the eye level of a human being. Even in the densest thicket there is almost always a clear space between the earth and the first low branches. So, although the passer-by is faced by an almost impenetrable screen of leaves and twigs, any number of unseen creatures may be watching his feet through dozens of ground-level spyholes. Any watcher willing and knowledgeable enough to squat patiently on the ground where he can peer under the leaves for the network of hidden paths and runways will see much to his advantage.

TENT CATERPILLARS

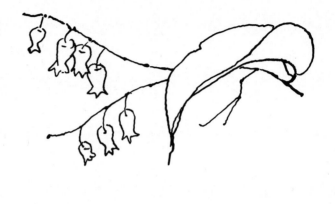

Tent Caterpillars

SOON AFTER the first warm spring rains, the bright silvery constructions made by the tent caterpillars begin to shine like out-of-season Christmas decorations in the forks of the wild cherry branches around the pond.

Protected from the weather by a hardened mass of foamy material insulating the inconspicuous egg deposits ringing the tips of slender twigs, the hundreds of young caterpillars have quietly waited out the winter—each in his own tiny egg cell. But soon after the first green shows at the tips of leaf buds, those who have escaped the attentions of the titmice, nuthatches, and other such hunters begin to gnaw their way out of their cramped quarters.

The first tiny caterpillar, so small as to be almost invisible, breaks through the sun-warmed crust and looks about. Bending and twisting, he works the kinks out of his system or takes a few experimental steps this way or that, learning to co-ordinate his complicated crawling equipment. With three pairs

of feet under his front end and a long unsupported middle section followed by three more pairs of feet, a caterpillar must put his best foot forward if he wants to get anywhere in the world.

Soon a half dozen more of the brood appear and they all set off, trudging head to tail down the branch to scout a location for their first "tent." Even at this very young stage each caterpillar spins out an almost invisible gossamer thread to mark his way. At every step or two the leader bobs his head, apparently tacking the line to the bark between his feet. And each one in the column does the same, putting down his line on top of or beside those already there, so that a constantly widening highway of silken threads marks their way.

Caterpillars are without protective weapons and the world is full of hungry neighbors. Spring weather, too, is notoriously changeable and they must have a rainproof roof over their heads as soon as possible.

These first scouts select a fork where three or four twigs branch out to serve as tent poles for their construction and then they go to work. At first they appear to be simply milling aimlessly about, accomplishing nothing.

However, a closer look shows that the performance isn't as aimless as it appears. From the bottom of the crotch they climb a twig to a certain height, hesitate a moment, then turn and trudge back down and up another twig to repeat the performance. At the turning place each caterpillar attaches a thread

firmly to the bark, then lets it reel out loosely behind him as he climbs down and across and up to
the next turning place where he attaches the other
end. At first these threads are almost invisible, but
as they dry they turn white and begin to shrink.
Each line shortens and tightens until it stretches in
a straight line across the angle of the fork, an inch
or two above the heads of the workmen.

In ones and twos and half dozens more new-
hatched caterpillars follow the ribbon of life lines
down to the work site and join the others at their
peculiar business. As the crowd grows, the network
of tightening lines finally forms a scaffolding strong
enough to support the weight of the workers. So
now they swarm over these flimsy foot ropes, carrying line after line in crisscross pattern over and
around the supporting twigs and the first flimsy
framework. As these new lines shrink in their turn
they form a strong open-work fabric of surprising
strength—wrapped tightly and neatly about the
supporting twigs.

By now the tent has taken shape, but it offers
little protection from wind, rain, or enemies. So,
stopping their busy coming and going, the caterpillars cling in masses to the outside of the fabric,
swinging their heads from side to side like small
clockwork toys. Advancing a fraction of an inch at
a time, they spin and attach loop after loop of fine
gossamer thread to the open work until the entire
construction is wind- and waterproof.

When at last the job is finished the colony enters

their new home through small openings left on the underside and gathers in a compact cluster to rest. At this stage the tent is a gleaming snowy white, stretching in smooth tight curves one half to three quarters of an inch above the heads of the sleeping caterpillars.

With no help or instruction from anyone, these brand-new caterpillars have managed a most complicated bit of building and it is easy for a watcher to convince himself that their instinct is infallible. But the truth is that, like everybody else, they do occasionally make errors of judgment.

One such colony spent half the morning building their small tent in the fork of a slender wild cherry, where several small branches joined the main trunk three or four feet from the ground. When finished it was the usual neat, little purselike caterpillar tent, light and airy inside.

But what the builders hadn't realized was that they'd built right over the broad band of life lines made by an older colony from above on their way down the trunk to feed on wild grape leaves near the ground. The newcomers had no more than gotten settled when the crowd below started straggling back up the tree. The first ones to arrive at the point where the life line disappeared under the new tent hesitated a moment, then cautiously fanned out over the roof and on to where their road reappeared above. Others found their way through the entrances of the small tent and blundered about inside until they were able to break out again near the top, tearing the fragile fabric to tatters. (This reminds one of the story of the people who built their house straddling the railroad track and had to put up with trains running through the living room.)

What happened to the newcomers is still a mystery. The small tattered tent was never rebuilt, nor was there any sign of another new one anywhere close by. Maybe they simply followed the larger ones home and moved in with them—or maybe a bird found them first and solved their problem the simple way.

The habit of depending on previously laid-down life lines sometimes leads tent caterpillars into very odd situations. A tall cherry tree sported one large tent near the top of the main trunk and another lower down, some six feet out toward the tip of a horizontal branch. Both colonies were in the habit of feeding in some growth clustered around the foot of the home tree, and a wide stripe on the reddish bark marked the way from each tent. Where the branch joined the trunk, the paths joined also and continued down the trunk in a single wider line. During sunny mornings or afternoons there would be a continual going and coming of stragglers from each of the tents to the pasture place.

At a time when there was much travel on this double road I cut away a six-inch strip, just below the joining, so that one road ran between the two nests, with no sign of the turn-off that had led downward. Travelers on the way to pasture now would come to the nonexistent fork, pause a bit with the characteristic swinging of the head, then continue along the unfamiliar road. It was impossible to tell what happened when the strangers appeared at their neighbor's tent—for at a little distance one caterpillar looks very like another. But for a while there was a great scurrying backward and forward from one tent to the other.

Stragglers returning from the feeding grounds began to gather at the bottom of the break in the main road, and before long, after much squirming and many false starts, one bold fellow crossed the bare spot laying down a new life line as he went, and the break was bridged so that business could go on as before.

In fine weather the young caterpillars alternate foraging trips in search of green leaves with spells of rest in or on their tent. Rainy days they stay warm and dry inside.

Their growth is very rapid and almost immediately they begin to feel the need of more living space, but instead of looking for a new location they simply build a new tent to enclose the old one. Traveling back and forth over the outside of the old fabric they spin thousands of new lines, attaching them to the same twigs as before, but at spots an inch or two higher. When they've finished they have a two-room tent, one inside the other, with a space of half an inch or so between the walls.

And as long as the caterpillars continue to grow they keep adding to their living quarters. The final tent may be as much as a foot from top to bottom and contain as many as a half-dozen progressively smaller and older envelopes, one inside the other.

RAIN

Soft Spring Rain

PEOPLE GENERALLY think of rain as something of a misfortune—a source of annoyance and possible discomfort. Of course farmers, gardeners, taxi drivers, and boys with new raincoats are an exception to this rule. But none the less, a drizzle on the day of a picnic is sure to bring on grumbles. And rain has been known to ruin completely garden parties, baseball games, horse races, political rallies, and other such outdoor affairs.

But down in the woods around the old millpond business goes on much as usual, in spite of the steady fall of soft spring rain. Fur gets wetter than feathers, so the squirrels and other fur-bearing animals stay under shelter—but the bird factory is going full blast. Sparrows, towhees, brown threshers, and other ground birds have simply moved from the little clearings and are stirring up the leaves and litter under the thickets. For a while a red-winged blackbird idles on the very top of a high white snag, taking advantage of the shower to clean and dress

19

his feathers while his mate continues to work on the nest in a grass tussock in the marsh below.

And in the middle of the downpour a crow flies low over the clearing carrying an unbroken blue egg in his beak. He seems so unruffled and so quietly pleased with himself and the rain that it is impossible to think harshly of him for being the thief that he obviously is.

In an unprotected fork of small branches growing from the bare trunk of a nearby juniper the bluejay sits patiently on her nest, soaking wet. Settling herself a little deeper into the ragged nest she watches as I set up the telescope under the protection of the jeep's canvas top. The words "TV Dinner," printed in red block letters on a neat cardboard square she has used to shore up the base of the structure, add a gay note to the weathered-looking mass of sticks and grass.

As we watch each other the male, with feathers as wet and bedraggled as hers, comes splashing through the gentle downpour to light on the edge of the nest and offer her some tidbit he's picked up on the way.

A persistent small tapping from the side hill above the abandoned road comes from where the nuthatches are busy at their house-building projects. In a stand of scattered young pines killed a year before by fire, three pairs are busy drilling nest holes fifteen or twenty feet above the ground.

The trees, four or five inches in diameter, are mostly spongy sapwood; but even so, these small

birds make slow progress. What even the smallest woodpecker would have finished in two or three afternoons has already taken them the better part of a week. While one works inside tapping away in desultory fashion, or looks idly about the neighborhood between trips to the door with chips, the other often hangs just outside, ignoring the steady rain, and carries on what seems to be an encouraging conversation. Taking frequent rest periods, both fly off to feed a while, often in the company of another pair.

The finished nest chambers are professional-looking jobs, the entrances—somewhat smaller than a quarter—leading into a gourd-shaped hollow four or five inches deep. No woodpecker does better.

Down nearer the edge of the water the mourning dove is considering building on what remains of a long-abandoned squirrel's nest in a twisted gum tree. She tramps unconcernedly back and forth over the shaky platform, paying no attention to the rain, while her mate whistles off on trip after trip in search of building material. Flying back with a twig in his bill, he lights on a branch within reaching distance, then proudly passes the treasure to her. He watches quietly while she takes the bit and moves it from one place to another, much like a lady trying to settle a new sofa. Often as not, either through accident or design, the twig falls overboard. But neither bird seems much concerned by such occurrences, and while the female resumes her absent-minded walking and rearrangement the male flies off for another load.

It is the thrush, however, who really makes the most of the wet day. Flying across the little clearing with a long banner of limp rain-soaked wrapping paper some litterbug has thrown out on the roadside, she drapes it in tasteful festoons over a dogwood branch to serve as a foundation for her nest. Tugging and hauling at the dead spikes of wild iris, she gathers great loads of the long, wet streamers and adds them to the wet paper so that they hang down saddle fashion a foot or more on either side of the branch. Then, on top of the saddle she twists other streamers in horizontal loops to make a base for the cup of the nest itself. This will be more carefully woven of finer material and finally plastered inside with mud from the edge of the pond.

The thrush builds successfully in dry weather, but her material is much easier to work into a firm structure when it is limp and heavy from the rain. Instead of taking two or three days to complete her building, as she often does in ordinary times, this nest was completed in one day.

A Sudden Shower

SUDDEN SHOWERS are no great problem for the birds who are going about their ordinary chores—their well-oiled feathers repel the rain as well as any raincoat. If the rain becomes too heavy for comfort they simply move into the protection of thickets, and a perching bird, finding his "roof" leaking directly overhead, merely moves an inch or two to a drier spot. But the bird brooding over eggs in her nest must stay where she is, rain or no rain.

So when the first gusts of wind running ahead of the dark rain clouds begin to rock the slender redbud branches under the old thrush's nest, she simply pushes herself a little deeper into the ragged cup and waits.

Shifting this way and that to meet the wind's changing directions, she keeps a watchful eye on the branches whipping and waving around her. And when the wind finally settles into one steady direction, bringing the first big raindrops, she shifts again to face straight into it. She has chosen the location of her nest very carefully, building it in one of the top forks of the redbud. The umbrella of wide leaves overhead keeps off the sun during the hottest part of the day, yet from beneath it she has a good view of all the surrounding neighborhood. And now as the rain drops roll and splash gently from one leaf to another on the way to the ground, she is kept dry except for a fine spray gathering in tiny silvery globules on the oily surface of her feathers.

As the weight of the rain increases, however, it drives down past the flimsy leaves and begins to beat steadily onto the nest and onto the thrush's back.

Feeling the wetness increasing, she works herself still deeper into the nest, until her tail and head stick almost straight up at either end. Partly spread-

ing her wings to cover the space between her body and the rim of the nest, she squinches her eyes tight shut and patiently sets herself to wait for the rain to stop.

The flicker inside the nest hole high up in the dead white snag is not troubled by the shower. She simply stirs a little over her eggs and listens drowsily to the rain drumming on the gray wood of her outside wall. Her mate, meanwhile, having nothing to do, hangs upside down on the dry underside of a nearby branch.

At the downy woodpeckers' doorway on the underside of an overhanging branch of the old mulberry tree, business goes on as usual. The nest hole is filled with young birds making excited soft, buzzing sounds in response to the rattle of the rain outside. The parents ignore the rain, making trip after trip across the pond to search the bark of dead trees for beetles and larvae to feed the hungry brood.

While the young birds are still in the nest the old ones go to considerable pains to see that they are protected from the rain. But as soon as they take their first steps out into the world the situation is changed. For young birds, leaving home is no gradual process—there is no such thing as taking a trial trip out into the neighborhood for the day, then returning to spend another night or two in the old nest. As a general thing the old birds try to lead the young directly to protected spots where they will have shelter from both weather and marauders while they learn the tricks of their trade. And for a few days they continue to feed and advise them. But, except for that, the young ones are on their own—when it rains they get wet the same as anybody else.

This morning the two young cuckoos in the turkey oak began their trip out into the world. With much soft-voiced encouragement from the old ones they left the nest, which looked more like a badly weathered oversize pancake than a home for small birds. They fluttered and teetered their way clumsily out toward the tip of the slender home branch. From there, after being fed and taking a short rest, they crossed the six-inch gap between the branch tip and the mass of wild grapevine hanging from the neighboring persimmon.

All morning long they climbed in short stages between feedings. Grasping the vine stems with their strong claws, they made their way along, hand over hand, to an airy perch at the very top of the old persimmon. From that high place they could look all about the neighborhood. They had just settled in precarious balance to rest after the long morning's trip from the nest ten feet below, when the same gusts that rocked the old thrush's nest in the nearby redbud began to shake their own limber perch.

Bobbing and fluttering, the two young cuckoos hung grimly on while the branch swung up and down and from side to side in irregular arcs.

When the rain started, the young ones huddled in their exposed place, looking uncomfortable and making occasional shrill-voiced complaints. The old birds, hurrying one after another in their silent, falconlike flights, gave them a last quick feeding, then disappeared into the protection of a thicket some distance off, leaving the small half-feathered birds to do as best they could.

When the rain did stop, after a half-hour or so, the old birds returned to find the young ones unconcernedly grooming and rearranging their bedraggled feathers as if getting drenched was an everyday occurrence.

The Big Blue Heron and the Rain

DURING the steady downpour the blue heron, instead of seeking shelter, goes unconcernedly about his business. His feathers protect him from the wet, and the rain brings frogs, salamanders, and small game out into the open, making hunting easy. Later, as the flow of the crooked marsh channels increases, he turns his attention to them. Fish there become less cautious as they take advantage of the rich harvest being washed along by the rising water. Or, if the

little streams begin to overflow their banks, flooding the marshy shallows alongside, he follows the rising water to hunt out the creatures whose hiding places have become uninhabitable.

So, while others wait for the rain to be over, the big blue heron feeds well. Then after the rain, when the less enterprising creatures return to their interrupted work, the heron stands about digesting his catch while he enjoys the sun and dresses his mud-splashed feathers.

The Spider's Peculiar Performance

THROUGH two weeks of dry, windy weather a green and creamy yellow spider has been halfheartedly tending a small web stretched horizontally between two bushes at the edge of a sun-baked clearing. Apparently she has made only a minimum of repairs to the structure, spending the greater part of her time huddled in her sleeping place under a leaf.

But one afternoon, when a change in the wind brought the beginning of a soft misty rain, she suddenly came to life and ran out to the middle of one of the long cables supporting her web. Hanging quietly upside down there she did nothing at all for a time and seemed to be simply enjoying the cool dampness. Then she began a series of curious washing movements with her long forelegs. This went on

for some minutes, and then she again hung motionless for a time before repeating whatever it was she was doing.

Absorbed as she was in her peculiar project, she made no objection to the big magnifying glass I focused on her intriguing performance. During her motionless periods a fine mist of almost invisible droplets collected on the hairs of her long forelegs. When she judged that there were enough of them, she began the washing movement. Carefully squeegeeing the moisture downward she soon collected a clear drop a little larger than a pinhead in the crook of one elbow. Then, carefully raising her bent arm toward her face, she quickly scooped the drop of water into her mouth with a shorter foreleg, like a boy licking cake frosting off his finger.

It seemed an odd way to go about getting a drink—but who was I to criticize?

As the rain increased, the thirsty spider came to life and hurried back along her cable to the dry waiting place under the leaves of the bush. But the big garden spider continued to hang head downward in the middle of her nearby web, ignoring the rain.

TURTLES

How the Turtle Lays Her Eggs

THE TURTLE is an egg-layer who never sees her children to know them or takes the slightest hand in their upbringing. However, she must be given credit for the care she takes to find a suitable spot for the nursery. She buries her eggs several inches in the ground where they'll be hatched by the heat of the sun, so she must locate a site with suitable drainage and not too much shaded by trees.

Around the nearby pond the trees and brush grow down to the water's edge on all sides, forcing the turtles to travel considerable distances up the hillsides in search of suitable clearings.

The abandoned woods road winding through the scrub oak is a favorite egg-laying place for the pond turtles. Careful tracing of an almost invisible trail of claw marks in the sandy places will often lead to a clutch of newly buried eggs. And careful digging into any place where the soil seems even slightly disturbed will sometimes bring others to light.

But knowing how to find the eggs after the

31

turtle has laid them and seeing exactly how she goes about burying them are two different matters. Her stolid, blundering look is misleading. Out on dry land the turtle is as wary and sneaky as a wild turkey. Every few steps she stops for a long careful look all about, and there seems to be nothing whatever wrong with her eyesight. At any suspicious sound or movement she freezes, so that only a very sharp eye can pick out her muddy shape and coloring from the shadows and dead leaves around her, and it takes very careful stalking to catch her at her business.

Naturally, then, I was pleased when a turtle came cautiously out into the road one steamy afternoon without seeing me idling in the shade of a thicket a few yards off. The spotting scope was already set up and focused on a whip-tailed lizard's burrow out in the sunshine, and while the turtle looked about for a location to suit her it was a simple matter to swing the scope onto her.

Having at last decided on a place she liked, the old turtle raised herself high on her braced front legs and stretched her neck to peer about in all directions for signs of danger. Then, while one hind leg supported the back of her shell, the other went to work scraping at the ground with short semicircular sweeps. The turtle's foot is surprisingly strong and flexible. With the sharp claws she first loosened and raked the dirt, then spreading and cupping the foot she used it like a spoon to scoop out the loosened material and pile it neatly at one side.

Alternately scooping and scraping, she sank a neat shaft a couple of inches across and five or six inches deep. In that sun-baked place, the ground, as she dug deeper, became too hard for even her strong claws. But she was prepared to deal with the problem; discharging some water from her bladder she waited a while until it had soaked and softened the dirt, then continued her digging. When she had dug as deep as she could reach with her leg fully extended, she began to widen the bottom of the shaft to make a chamber for the eggs.

When that was done, still without having moved out of her tracks or looked back to inspect her work, she began depositing the eggs, letting them drop haphazardly to the bottom of the gourd-shaped hole. A turtle may lay from three to as many as a dozen eggs at a time. This one laid six, then immediately began scooping the dirt back into the hole with the same handy foot as before. Every few minutes she stopped and jiggled up and down on this foot to tamp and pack the loose dirt firmly into place. When the hole was filled she scratched over the remaining dirt with one foot and then the other, blurring the faint outline of the little mound. Then, pivoting on her shell to face back the way she had come, she crawled away home without so much as a backward look. Her work had been so neatly done that only by the most careful examination of the area was it possible to find the slight disturbance in the sandy ground.

All turtles take their family responsibilities lightly, washing their hands of the whole business as soon as they've dug a hole and buried a clutch of eggs in some sunny spot. But there seems to be a difference of opinion among the various kinds of turtles as to the proper way of doing this. The mud turtle, instead of digging a neat round shaft as the pond turtle does, literally plows herself into the ground. Scraping the dirt away from behind and below her with her hind feet, she backs downward at a sharp angle until only her head and the front edge of her shell are visible. Then, when her egg laying is finished she simply crawls out, letting the loose earth fall back into place, covering the eggs with no effort on her part.

The Snapping Turtle

THE SNAPPING turtle is a hardheaded lone wolf sort of citizen. He's not one to climb out on a floating log and take the sun with his neighbors as the pond turtles do. Instead, he spends much of his time cruising stealthily about just beneath the surface of the water or lying in wait among the waterweeds on the bottom of the pond.

Occasionally, if the light is right, he can be seen

suspended motionless in the water below the lily pads. With legs and tail hanging limply, he seems to be resting and harmless, making no move except at intervals when he slowly extends his neck and cautiously raises the very tip of his nose above the surface for a breath of air. The long trailers of moss hanging from his shell and the pale unhealthy color of his underside blend with the murky shadows and he becomes almost invisible. But, for all his stolid appearance, he can strike swiftly and accurately, so that any small creature making the mistake of swimming too close will probably do the rest of its traveling inside the turtle.

In spite of being something of a homebody, the snapping turtle does do considerable traveling overland, especially in wet weather when the streams are overflowing their banks. Then he leaves his home pond and goes out in search of flooded meadows to take advantage of the good hunting such places provide.

For a few days, until the water goes down, he plows his way back and forth through the drowned grass and weeds harvesting field mice, young birds, and stranded fish; earthworms driven from their homes by the flood; and even an occasional hunting snake.

Not long ago I watched an old snapper trying to cross the highway ahead of me at a time when traffic was heavy. Every few steps his progress was interrupted by a passing automobile. A pond or box turtle in such a situation usually pulls his head and legs into his shell and hopes for the best—which often enough turns out to be the last decision he ever makes. And the serpent, in spite of his reputation for wisdom, seldom realizes until too late that an automobile has no feeling about snakes one way or the other—and often gets a broken back for his foolishness as he tries at the last minute to scurry to safety. But the snapping turtle is made of sterner stuff. He turns to face his enemy as it bears down on him, bracing his powerful hind legs and hissing defiance.

People who do not hesitate to run over an ordinary turtle, a snake, or even a dog on the pavement usually try to avoid hitting a snapper. Possibly his rough shell and pugnacious stance convey the impression that an auto, despite its weight advantage, just might come out second best in a head-on encounter.

And now, as the cars passed over with their wheels going safely on either side of him, the snapper, unimpressed, did his best to disembowel each one in its turn. Striking powerfully upward to the full reach of his long neck and front legs, he slashed viciously with his hooked beak at what he seemed to consider the creature's vulnerable under parts. Probably it was lucky for him that even the lowest-slung automobile was several inches beyond his reach. In spite of his confidence it seemed an uneven match, so after watching a while I picked him up and gave him a jeep ride to a flooded meadow down the road a way.

SMALL CLEARING
AND SUNKEN ROAD

The Whip-tailed Lizards

FROM WHERE the jeep was parked in a shady spot there was, at first, no movement of any kind to be seen in the little clearing. Even the telescope picked up only an occasional ant coming out of the dense shade of scattered leaf clumps standing up from the ground-running wisteria—or a cruising dragonfly tacking across the open space a time or two before going on.

But a close look at the loose sand revealed criss-crossing lines and small spidery tracks of a dozen sizes and shapes. And there were burrows too, some with fresh dirt piles close by and others in clean-swept areas, their black shadowy openings ranging in size from an inch in diameter to the width of the head of a kitchen match. Some of the inhabitants were away on temporary business while the rest were watching from various hiding places. Strangers, especially people, are not quickly accepted in neighborhoods such as this.

After a quarter of an hour a blurry shadow

scuttled through the loose leaves under the thicket and came to a stop behind a small stick lying at the far edge of the clearing. It was the whip-tailed lizard. From his partial concealment he peered intently at the jeep while I admired the dusty orange lines down his back and the pale turquoise color of the plates on his chops and throat. And now he looked about with a faint expression of anxiety— this lizard has larger, more expressive eyes than most of the other varieties—then carefully backed out of sight. In a few minutes he reappeared in the shade of one of the tiny wisteria clumps to watch and consider some more. Seen through the big glass it was easy to think of the wisteria as some kind of tropical tree and the lizard as a dragonlike, monster reptile from some far-off time. In spite of his small size, his front feet are strongly built and armed with surprisingly heavy claws for digging in hard ground.

At last crossing the sun-baked clearing in short rushes, he zigzagged across open areas, stopping every few steps to peer about him. Hunting for earthworms and soft-bodied insects he went under dead leaves, searched grass clumps, and rattled around under old brush piles left by the timber cutters.

Later the female showed up, a smaller dusty-tan-colored lizard without the handsome turquoise markings of the male. Both seemed to hunt in circles, returning every quarter of an hour or less to the entrance of their burrow. Each time one of the lizards returned, he or she would disappear into the tunnel for a few minutes. Then, after standing for

a moment with head and shoulders outside for a careful look around, the lizard would go back to the hunt.

This went on until the sun beat down from straight overhead and the heat became oppressive. Then both disappeared into the burrow, the doorway was plugged with sand, and no more was seen of them until later in the afternoon.

The Young Tiger Beetle

THE DIGGER WASPS, the mining bees, the little gray-leaf cutter, and other insects of similar habits probably never, never see their young ones—or even recognize them if they happen to meet. But they do at least go to the trouble of building a nursery and stocking it with food. The tiger beetle, however, takes her responsibilities even more lightly and pampers her children not at all.

She is a slim, long-legged little creature, with a hard-shelled body about a half-inch in length. And while her neighbors spend endless hours at their excavating and food storing, stopping only for an occasional sip of nectar, she ranges back and forth across the little clearing in search of meat to satisfy her terrible appetite. Now and again she interrupts her hunting for a moment, deposits an egg just under the surface of the ground, then goes on about her affairs.

When the young one hatches, some days later, he is entirely on his own. If he wants food and shelter he has to provide them for himself. He comes equipped with powerful biting jaws and a heavily armored flat, sloping forehead, but the remainder of his body is soft and grublike. So now he stretches, perhaps commenting on the hard life of a baby tiger beetle, and starts digging his way to the surface. Then, after a quick look around to see what kind of a world he has inherited, he sets about deepening and improving the temporary shaft from which he has just emerged.

He carries upstairs in his heavy jaws load after load of tiny pellets of dirt mixed with saliva. When he reaches the surface he gives his head a flirt and flings the trash well out of his dooryard. As soon as he has drilled himself a neat shaft just the diameter of his body in width and dropping straight into the ground an inch or two, he settles down to his main business—which is to feed himself.

Full grown he will be a swift, well-armored beetle, stalking and running down game like the tiger for whom he is named. But now he is a little crawling creature, and his only armor is the flat plate on his head; if he ventures out of the burrow his soft afterparts will surely be bitten by someone. So he plays a waiting game. Lying in the doorway with his armored forehead blocking the entrance and his jaws flat on the ground, he is almost invisible to passers-by until it is too late. Sooner or later some insect—and it doesn't matter much what

kind—is sure to come blundering by. The tiger lies in wait until the range is point-blank and then, like lightning, the fierce jaws lash out and clamp down on the unsuspecting stranger. If his victim is a small creature he simply drops with it to the bottom of the hole to have his meal in peace.

The young tiger has a huge appetite, however, and he sometimes tangles with powerful neighbors who are shy about visiting his dining room and have to be forcibly persuaded. In such cases a heavy antagonist may threaten to pull him out of his hole. But he is prepared for such emergencies, with a set of sharp spines set into his back about halfway down the length of his body. He has only to arch his back, forcing the spines into the burrow wall, and he is safely anchored for the toughest tug of war.

In the end the result is almost always the same. The stranger goes down the hole, and the only sign of him that is ever seen again is an odd piece of wing cover, shell, or other inedible part tossed into the dooryard a day or two later.

The grub will probably live in his burrow for the better part of two years before getting his full growth and turning into a beetle. Periodically he outgrows his skin and has to slough it off. At such times he wants privacy, so he tightly plugs his door-way with sand and returns to the chamber at the bottom of the shaft until the finicky job is finished. Then, when he is finally outfitted with a new and roomier skin, he unplugs his doorway only to discover the shaft is now too small for comfort. So he begins scraping away at the walls with his jaws—mixing the dirt with saliva to make transportation of the pellets easier—until he has enlarged the hole to fit his new dimensions.

The Leaf-cutting Bee

THE LEAF CUTTER, often called the rose leaf cutter, is a small, dark solitary bee with soft gray fur, who goes about her affairs so quietly it's hard to believe she is a cousin of the swashbuckling bumble bee.

People who grow roses complain bitterly about her habit of cutting neat circles and ovals out of the leaves of their prize bushes, but beyond that, few even know who she is or what her habits are.

Her liking for rose leaves is probably an acquired taste, for in the woods she seems to favor the leaves of pokeweed, redbud, and occasionally even dogwood. The bee who is working here at the edge of the little clearing usually begins her cutting and carrying late in the hot forenoons, when the leaves hang limp and wilted from their stems. She is another of the insects who lay an egg along with a food supply for the larva when it hatches, then disclaim all further responsibility. However, since her young ones will probably be in their nursery for several months, she takes more care than does the big wasp who has just finished digging a hole beside the path. The wasp simply buries a grasshopper in a chamber at the bottom of the shaft, attaches an egg to it, refills the burrow, and hopes for the best.

The leaf cutter is broad-minded in her choice of location for her nest chambers. Sometimes she'll use a crevice underneath the bark of a handy tree or the tunnel of one of the larger wood-boring beetles. This bee is using the burrow that was dug and then, for some reason, abandoned by the big yellow-and-black wasp.

Whatever the location, once she has found or prepared a tunnel suitable for a nursery chamber, the bee flies up to a leaf, twisting so as to grasp its lower edge with her feet. Hanging upside down and using her mandibles as scissors, she cuts out a neat oval a little longer than her body. Like the man in the story who saws off the branch he's sitting on, she cuts away the part of the leaf she's hanging from. In her case, however, it is a deliberate policy; as she takes the last snip and drops free, she flips herself right side up and flies off with the piece of leaf held neatly underneath her body.

She carries the oval length of green inside the nursery and presses it lengthwise against the side of the chamber like wallpaper. She continues adding pieces until she has built a tight, hollow cylinder just a little larger than her body in diameter. Each bit of leaf carefully overlaps the one before, and in the last layers the seams appear to be lightly cemented with a brown, gummy substance to make them water- and parasite-proof.

When the diameter of the tiny cylinder finally suits her, she begins cutting perfect circles out of the leaves instead of ovals. These are carefully fitted and cemented, layer after layer, into the end of the cylinder. When that is done she is ready to start gathering the mixture of pollen and nectar that will feed the larva when it hatches.

Hundreds of trips later, when she has filled the cylinder with a firmly packed mass of food as large as her body, she lays a single egg against the cache and then returns again to her leaf cutting. With more circular-shaped bits of leaves she fits a tight cover several layers thick over the open end of the cylinder, sealing it tightly at the seams.

For several days she worked more or less steadily in and out of the wasp's burrow, and later, when I dug it up I found she had built six cylinders, placed neatly end to end in a horizontal side gallery a couple of inches below the surface.

One morning in the studio I finally traced a curious, small gnawing sound to a little cardboard box of sand sitting among the jumble of brushes, paint jars, old turtle shells, and dead beetles on the worktable.

Last fall, digging into a sandy bank riddled with the burrows of whip-tailed lizards, I'd found a handful of a leaf cutter's newly built cells inside the hollow of a finger-sized rotted root. I brought them home in the little box of sand where they'd spent the winter on the worktable. One of the cells had been dug out by some visitor and left on top of the sand. And now the dried brown cell was being gnawed at from the inside—a well-spaced, unhurried crunching. After a bit the beginning of a thin dark line appeared at the bottom edge of the seal between the plug and the side wall. By looking closely it was possible to see a tiny black mandible reaching from inside to snip at the dried material of the cell.

Occasionally the shiny sharp point would be withdrawn while the bee inside shoved against the plug to widen the crack a little. Then she would return to her patient cutting.

A mud dauber wasp cutting her way out into the world from her mud chamber accompanies her cutting and chipping with intervals of high-pitched buzzing, but this bee worked in silence except for the small sounds of sawing.

It took her over half an hour to cut three quarters of the way around the seal, but at last with a shove of her shoulders she pushed the lid back on the remaining hinge and her door was open. She lay on her back, apparently having done the cutting by swiveling her head on her shoulders. For a while she drew back from the opening, seeming to be struggling to free herself from something inside the cell. After some struggle accompanied by a soft silky whirring, she walked daintily out onto the drawing board, an exact copy of the stubby little gray-and-black bees I'd seen before.

For some time she sat on the board cleaning and polishing her legs, head, and antennae and groom-

ing her hairy back and sides. As she worked, tiny brown flakes of some stiff filmy material collected on the board underneath her.

Finally satisfied with her appearance, she flew out the open screen door and into the sunshine, leaving behind the empty cell half filled with a bed of spongy, brown corklike material.

The Peculiar Thievery of Mining Bees

FOR SOME DAYS a number of fuzzy black mining bees with brownish-gold shoulder humps that give them somewhat the look of miniature buffalo have been going about family business in the baked red clay of the sunken road.

Buzzing and muttering, a bee will laboriously drive a shaft a quarter of an inch in diameter and a couple of inches deep into the red clay. Sometimes she uses part of the waste, moistened with saliva, to build a chimneylike turret half to three quarters of an inch high around the mouth of the diggings. Then, at the bottom she hollows out a round chamber the size of a large marble.

When the walls have been smoothed and the bottom cleaned, she begins a long series of foraging trips out into the weed patches and among the flowering bushes. Returning with her leg pockets

bulging with pollen she hurries down to the cellar, stays a few moments, and reappears empty-handed. It may take her a day or more to pack the cavity full, and it's probable that she mixes the pollen with nectar as she kneads and packs it firmly into place. If the clay is carefully dug away from the storage chambers after she has finished, a firm, damp golden ball about the consistency of cold corn meal mush can be found. To this food supply she has attached a single egg, then sealed up the shaft with a plug of saliva-moistened clay. The young one hatches in a few days and eats his or her way through the ball of nectar-soaked pollen; then in the space left by the disappearance of the food supply he pupates. In due time he digs his way to the surface, a fully formed bee.

As a rule the small colony is a scene of quiet, orderly activity. But one morning while I watched, a peculiar piece of business was transacted in three burrows located in a rough triangle about two feet on a side. A bee carrying nothing went into one of the burrows and in a few minutes came out with her abdomen plastered with flakes and crumbs of the pollen-nectar mixture. Apparently the material was too sticky to be carried in the leg baskets used for dry pollen. Hauling the clumsy load she hurried to her own burrow, disappeared for a moment, then reappeared empty-handed and hustled back to the first burrow for another load. She made eight or nine such trips into the neighbor's cellar, coming out empty-handed the last time, apparently having

completely emptied the pantry. Then she began
hurriedly picking up the yellow flecks and crumbs
she'd dropped on the ground between the two
burrows. While she was an inch or so from her own
doorway, still busy in her housewifely task of
gathering up the last scattered bits of her loot,
another bee swooped down past her and went un-
invited into her doorway. Reappearing after a
moment with a load of the stolen pollen mixture,
the newcomer hurried with it to *her* burrow,
disappeared downstairs for a moment, then returned
quickly for more. But by now the first bee had
recovered from her surprise and made for the
intruder to drive her off. Clinching in the air they
fell to the ground, buzzed and struggled about for
a bit, then separated. The first bee flew off into the
weeds while the newcomer returned to the business
of carrying off her neighbor's stolen treasure. She
seemed to carry bigger loads than her neighbor had,
and in six more trips cleaned the place out. After
the last trip she spent some time inside her own
place, probably laying her egg and making last-
minute finishing touches on the food arrangements,
then began plugging the shaft. Carefully and
unhurriedly troweling the tiny gobbets of moistened
clay into place with her mandibles, she filled the
hole to the level of the ground, smoothed the surface, then flew off as if this sort of thing happened
every day.

Where the owner of the original pollen supply in
the first burrow was while this was going on, or

what she thought when she came home and found
her cellar empty, is still a mystery.

The Eye Is Difficult To Camouflage

THE PECULIAR habits of the birds belonging to the
goatsucker family (the whippoorwill, the chuckwill's-widow, and the nighthawk) make them more
than ordinarily dependent on the completeness of
their camouflage. Being highly specialized insect
catchers who do all their feeding on the wing, their
feet are weak and poorly developed so they are
unable to perch as other birds do. Hunting mostly
in the dusk and through the night, they spend their
days on the ground or huddled lengthwise on the
flat surface of some handy tree limb. And at nesting
time the old bird simply selects what seems to her
a suitable clear space and lays her two eggs on the
ground. All during the brooding period the old
bird, and later the young ones, would appear to be
completely at the mercy of any passing hunter.
These birds, however, can become invisible on bare
ground, with no difficulty whatever.

A chuckwill had a nest, if it could be called that,
on the slope just above the abandoned road. I
discovered it only by accident when she suddenly
fluttered out from underfoot, just avoiding being
stepped on. Flying off in soft, bat-like fashion, she
seemed to be trying to distract my attention from

the single pale pink egg. There was no trace of any nest, and the egg simply lay there in the middle of the tiny clearing.

Later watching from the shelter of a nearby bush, it should have been an easy matter to locate such a dark bird against the lighter background of the smooth pine straw. But a careful look with the binoculars revealed no sign of either bird or egg. The stump I had carefully marked as a guide was in plain sight, and the egg had been less than two feet to the right of that. The clearing itself was no more than six feet wide by eight or ten feet long, bordered by a mass of old grapevine on one side and the fallen trunks of some dead pines on the others. Yet, even with the twenty-power scope, an inch-by-inch examination of the clear space showed no sign of the bird. There were three or four half-decayed pine cones scattered about, a few oddly shaped bits of dead wood half buried in the litter, a gray-green weed, a half-dozen old oak leaves, and nothing else. The only possible explanation seemed to be that the chuckwill had picked up the egg in her mouth—a thing she is said to sometimes do—and carried it to a safer place.

And then from one of the brownish-gray humps a tiny sparkle like sunlight reflected from a sliver of glass gave the bird away. In the center of the scope's field was now a wide-open shiny black eye, and as if by some magic the entire bird appeared. The stiff pale whiskers around her mouth, the tiny beak, and even the edge of the wing and the bulge of the breast feathers could all be plainly seen.

Instead of trying to match the color of the background to become invisible, she had simply become something else. Flattened on the ground, with her eyes shut and her feathers artfully bunched and disarranged, her lumpy shapelessness and soft mottling of warm browns, black, pinkish gray, and cream made her indistinguishable from the old pine cones and lumps of rotting wood scattered about her.

And every time the performance was repeated the result was always the same. As long as she kept her eyes closed it was impossible, after looking away even for a moment, to say for sure exactly which of the objects scattered about on the ground was the bird. But as soon as she raised one eyelid even a slit, her cloak of invisibility was destroyed. And when it rained, her soaked and darkened feathers still matched the new dark wetness of the wood and pine cones on the ground around her.

But the brooding chuckwill doesn't depend entirely on her ability to become invisible, effective as it is. A small dog wandering through the little clearing the other day got what was probably the fright of his life when he unwittingly came too close to her.

While I watched her through binoculars, she watched the approach of the dog through a half-open eye—but the only movement she made was an almost imperceptible stir as she settled herself

more closely onto the egg. The dog trotted along in idle zigzag fashion, apparently neither seeing nor scenting the bird. She still made no sign when he came within a couple of feet of where she waited, and it seemed that he would probably pass by without discovering she was there.

Then the dog must have stepped over what the bird considered the boundary of her territory, and she went into action. In a sudden explosive movement she fluffed her feathers so that they stuck out in all directions, nearly doubling her size. Her wings flapped out on either side in a peculiar bent-elbowed stance while she raised and spread her tail feathers into a ragged fan. Then, to add to the frightening performance, she opened wide her great gash of a mouth, exposing the pinkish white inside, and hissed. The startled dog did not wait to find out what dreadful thing had sprung up so suddenly almost in his very face—he simply left. From a safe distance he turned back and halfheartedly barked once or twice. But when the old bird shook her feathers and hissed again, he lost all further interest —and disappeared into the nearby thicket. The chuckwill held her fearsome pose for some time longer, then little by little she resumed her former compact, lumpy shape, closed her eye, and disappeared completely.

Two young nighthawks, almost fully feathered but still unable to fly, played much the same game with me on a soft, drizzly morning just after day-

light. Crossing one of the small white-sand patches scattered through the scrub oak, I must have nudged one of the young birds with my shoe. The first I knew of his presence was when he suddenly raised his long, slender wings straight up over his back in a curious back-to-back gesture and stumbled forward a few steps with his mouth wide open, hissing in fierce fashion.

He seemed convinced that he was indeed a bloodcurdling sight—and considering his small size he wasn't far wrong. After a few minutes he slowly folded his wings and settled onto the sand with his stubby tail flat on the ground and his head pulled deep into the ruffled feathers on his shoulder and breast. Then, as the chuckwill had done, he slowly closed his eyes and "disappeared."

Squatting to get a closer look at this bird, I touched what appeared to be a patch of lichen, and discovered the second bird instead. As my hand touched his feathers, he repeated the raised-winged hissing gesture of the first one, then settled and disappeared again.

The sand there was sparsely dotted by small hand-sized patches of wire grass, gray-green lichen, and scattered bits of oak leaves in all stages of decomposition. And the mottled pattern of the young birds, grayer over-all than the chuckwill, blended perfectly with the other bits. By continuing to watch one bird steadily after he closed the shiny black eye, it was still possible to see what he was— but look aside for a second, or from one to the other, and it was no longer possible to say for sure which were the birds and which the tiny tussocks of leaves and lichen. Sooner or later, however, an eye would slowly open and give the bird's location away.

The wood duck's camouflage is of a showier kind, especially that worn by the drake. The female's soft gray-brown and white is entirely suitable for the grass-grown shallows and small pools among the dead stumps and snags where she brings up her young ones. But the drake's snappy get-up of iridescent green, white, rose, ocher, and black seems much too garish to blend with any background. When he idles and preens himself in a shady place, however, the patches of vivid color effectively break up his outline so that only by some small movement is he likely to catch the attention of an observer.

The lily-choked areas of open water are among his favorite feeding places, and there his bright colors blend so perfectly with the broken greens, reds, and yellow-browns of the tumbled lily pads that it takes an unusually sharp eye to discover him.

During the last days of summer and early fall the nearly grown young ones gather in small groups to feed and play here in the pond. The first plumage of both young drakes and females is a faded imitation of the mother's sober outfit. But now the young drakes begin to molt and to take on their grown-up appearance.

The change takes place in a peculiar and un-

predictable sequence. While still wearing his dull duckling color one will suddenly appear with a startling deep-green crown patch perhaps, while another sports a touch of orange on his beak or the bright red-orange eye of the adult drake. But no matter in what order, bit by bit they add dark head feathers, rose breast, white throat-and-cheek markings, ocher side patches, and all the rest of the wood duck trimmings. And in a surprisingly short time the comic, half-finished look disappears and they are ready for business.

Meanwhile the females, with their white eye rings and throat patches, take on something of the wild look of deer. It is always an exciting and startling thing to be searching the edges of the rank marsh grass with the telescope and suddenly spot a shiny black—or orange—eye with its dramatic white ring, peering straight into the lens from between two grass stems.

The least bittern is another bird that has the ability to disappear before your very eyes. Out in the open he displays soft golden brown undersides and throat, with rich darker markings on his head, along the top of his neck, and on his back.

In the late afternoon he often comes across the pond to light nearby on a small ragged brush pile at the edge of the water. If he happens to notice the jeep he draws himself to his full height with his bill pointing straight up and his yellow eyes staring ahead like two beads sewed on either side of his

head. For long minutes he'll hold his stakelike pose while he considers the probability of danger. Then, if satisfied that there is none, he pulls his neck down and slowly steps into the stand of marsh grass. Here, instead of wading, he walks several inches above the surface of the water by grasping the coarse grass stems with his toes, moving so quietly about his hunting that the small fish and frogs below never see him until too late.

Screened by the outer curtain of grass clumps, his outline becomes so softened, and the pattern of his coloring blends so perfectly with the various warm greens, russets, and yellows, that even as you watch he becomes invisible for minutes at a time. That dark spot—is it a dead brown leaf or the patch on top of the bittern's head? And the soft, warm yellow—is that a handful of dead grass or the bittern's breast? Then he stretches his neck to snap a dragonfly passing too close overhead and once more his whole body is visible.

For a while he comes out to hang onto the outside of the grass screen, peering down into the water, heron fashion, waiting patiently for some small fish or frog to come within spearing distance. Even when he hunts out in the open, his movements are so deliberate and his poses so closely resemble the shapes of dead sticks that lie about that, until he moves, it takes a sharp and experienced eye to find him. And often enough it is only a small sparkle of reflected light from his bright yellow eye that gives him away.

VISITORS

The Otter Fishing

FOR A YEAR or more an otter has been a more or less regular visitor to the pond. At ten-day or two-week intervals I could count on seeing his tracks in the mud around the beaver dam or find signs of his having investigated old bank burrows abandoned by the beavers when the falling water level left the entrances exposed. Other signs of his visits were areas of flattened grass where he'd rolled about to dry his fur, and scats containing fish bones and crawfish shells. Occasionally it was possible to catch a glimpse of him from a distance doing a bit of last-minute fishing or enjoying the early-morning sunshine before holing up for the day. Otherwise he might as well have been invisible for all anyone ever saw of him.

Then, one afternoon there was an unusual, violent surging in the water alongside an abandoned beaver lodge just below the road. The pond there comes almost to the foot of the road embankment, which is fifteen or twenty feet high, so the jeep made a perfect grandstand seat.

61

On warm, drizzly afternoons the old muskrat living in a burrow at the side of the beaver lodge occasionally comes out for one of his rare spells of playing with his family. While he swims good-naturedly about, the drab gray kits race around him, diving to attack him from underneath, or clambering onto his back, playing a muskrat version of "King of the Mountain."

But this disturbance was greater than a muskrat family would make, so it was possible that a beaver was planning to take possession of the vacant lodge. Then, the water surged again ahead of a racing blanket of tiny bubbles circling the lodge from the far side, and there was no longer any doubt about who the visitor was—an otter.

A beaver can swim with considerable speed underwater, and a certain number of bubbles often mark his path—but his pace is comparatively sedate and the bubbles he leaves are scattered and of various sizes. The otter, on the other hand, darts about like a huge fish, leaving behind him a characteristic trail of thousands of tiny bubbles all of one size. An old farmer told me of once watching the place where an otter was fishing and of being able to follow the creature's actions by the wide streak of little "blubbers" that boiled up behind him. That seems a perfect word for them.

So now the line of "blubbers" snaked around the near side of the lodge, circled a submerged stump, and stopped as the round, grapefruit-sized head of an old otter popped up between the close-set trunks of

two gum trees growing out of the water. After a
quick look about, he slid out of sight again and
the line of bubbles shot under a sunken brush pile.
For a while the area rocked from his passage, and
water and bubbles boiled up first in one place and
then in another as he twisted and turned in search
of drowned passageways.

Between trips he climbed out onto a half-sunken
log to rest a bit or to eat whatever he'd caught. In
the shadows there and with his fur wet and black,
he was almost indistinguishable from the twisted
black shapes of the exposed roots and snags. After
some smacking and crunching, he wiped his spiky
whiskers and worked on his fur a little before sliding
smoothly back into the water. The water boiled up
again and the blanket of bubbles streaked back
under the brush pile. Sometimes, after the otter had
made a few turns, the line of bubbles streaked
straight across one of the patches of open water, or
whipped around the standing trees like a racing
boat turning a pylon. Or, again, he might swim
straight at a tree, then reverse himself in a racing
turn—Olympic fashion—and return to the brush
pile.

The otter was diligently working at his trade,
trying to catch enough fish for his supper, but from
the bank it seemed to be as much play as work.
Much of the time he appeared to be simply swimming for the pure fun of it—putting on an exhibition
of speed and fancy work among obstacles just for
his own amusement. Most of the time he swam

below the surface of the water, his progress marked only by the swirling bubbles. But occasionally he'd appear on top, swimming in undulating fashion, like a lively miniature sea serpent. After half an hour of this violent action, he loafed for a while on the log, arranging his wet fur, or listening to the late-afternoon sounds of the swamp, then swam off upstream.

The Heron and the Egret

LATE SUMMER is a sort of vacation time for the egrets, herons, and other waders. With their young ones grown and self-supporting, they are free to take solitary trips about the country visiting old fishing places and investigating new ones. With only themselves to feed, they now have time to loaf and groom their feathers or just to stand on some high snag idly watching their neighbors at work.

A great blue heron was the first one to appear here this summer from the nesting colonies deeper in the swamps. Being a little early he had some trouble with local residents who were still busy bringing up their second broods. One of the favorite heron lookouts is an old white snag standing high above a thicket of second-growth gum. But when this old blue heron arrived, a pair of flickers still had young ones in a nest hole up near the top.

Ordinarily the neighbors in such a place pay

little attention to well-behaved visitors. But nesting time is a different matter. So now, no sooner had the heron gotten himself settled for a session of sunning and peering about than a flicker zoomed past his head, breaking his train of thought and causing him to lose his precarious balance. He had no sooner resettled himself with a great deal of clumsy flapping and flouncing than the flicker whizzed past his face again. In the end it was easier to look for another place than to put up with continual harassment, so he moved to the dead top of a smaller gum tree nearby.

That was by no means the end of trouble with his neighbors, however. The red-winged blackbirds were still nesting in little grass hummocks scattered in the marshy places where the heron liked to stalk about in search of frogs and small fish. So he never knew when he'd suddenly find himself the center of attention at a gathering of birds diving threateningly at his back and raising a great clamor. Even when he obligingly flapped off in slow dignified flight, the quarrelsome birds often followed him for a considerable distance. And the kingbirds attacked him for no apparent reason at all, as he flew over on some harmless errand of his own.

But these were minor annoyances, and the pond was otherwise a peaceful place, well supplied with fish, frogs, and dragonflies. The heron spent long hours in the hot sunshine striding in slow motion through the shallows—or freezing for minutes at a time waiting for some likely bite to come within spearing range. Usually the game he found was small and needed only to be flipped into the air, caught headfirst, and swallowed. But now and again he caught a fish big enough to give him trouble—one so heavy that he had difficulty holding it out of the water.

Dealing with such a fish, he held it for a time in the air, gripped firmly crosswise in his bill, apparently waiting until exposure to the air had slowed it down somewhat. But the weight was more than his neck could support for long, and little by little he had to lower it until at last the fish was in the water again. By the time the heron's neck muscles were rested the fish, too, was revived by the few whiffs of water through his dried gills, and the struggle started all over.

When he'd caught the fish, the heron was standing in water so deep he looked more like a swan than what he was—and now he flapped and clambered to the top of a low stump with his load. But even there the fish's weight was more than he could manage; sooner or later he had to rest his neck. Lowered to the top of the stump, between the heron's feet, the fish slipped down to the water dragging the bird's head with it, and was revived as before. The struggle went on for three quarters of an hour before either the heron gave up or the fish broke the grip of the beak and escaped.

Between spells of fishing, the heron often stood in some clear place on the muddy flats just sunning himself. Facing the sun he'd straighten his neck to

its full length, tilting his head to expose the underside of his chin and letting his half-opened wings
droop limply around his knees. At such times he
looked as though he was standing in a pile of some-
body's laundry.

After sunning his feathers thoroughly he'd shake
himself violently, until he appeared to be twice his
usual size, with every feather standing straight out
from his body. Then he'd oil and flatten them one
by one and press them back into place with his
beak. In the process any number of small, downy
white feathers became detached. These, blowing
about in the slight breeze, seemed to fascinate
a family of young kildeers. Running back and forth
on their stilty legs, they interrupted their feeding to
chase the things and discuss them in their high
piping voices.

For a few days the big blue idled about the pond,
then one morning at dawn—or perhaps on a bright
moonlit night—he flapped off to spend some time
at some other such resort.

The big blue heron, with his gray-blue coloring
touched with warm ocher and bits of white, blends
into the background so that even on the marshy
flats he is hard to spot, and when he stands frozen
among the whitened stumps he becomes about as
nearly invisible as it is possible to be.

But when the egret drops by, his pure white
plumage and flashy yellow bill make him a sight
that is hard to miss. He too strides about in
dignified fashion through the shallows. But his

technique is somewhat different from the blue heron's. Much of his hunting seems to be for small creatures living in the muddy bottom.

Wading slowly in the shallow water, he takes a cautious step, then stretches his neck at a stiff forty-five-degree angle while he gently stirs the deep muck with his foot to flush out frogs and other small game.

From a distance he appears during this curious performance to be continually staring off into space. But possibly he is able to arrange his eyes so as to focus on the water directly below his jaws. At any rate, every now and then he suddenly breaks his star-gazing pose to make a lightning thrust deep into the roiled water, reaching for some tidbit or other. And after each strike, whether it is successful or not, he daintily rinses his long yellow beak before going on.

Once, after a quarter of an hour of this slow and cautious progress among the drowned gray stumps, he suddenly, for no apparent reason, reversed his course. Striking excitedly in all directions he seemed to have somehow stirred up a surprising choice of targets. Through the glass it was possible to see that each time the egret stepped forward a small but violent disturbance roiled and stirred the water just ahead of him.

The mystery of the peculiar performance was solved when, after several repetitions, a huge turtle's head appeared above the surface during one of the pauses. Apparently he had been awakened from his siesta in the mud by the egret's gently probing foot, and in his efforts to escape this annoyance he made a great stir in the shallow water. Wherever he went the bird followed, taking advantage of the windfall of scurrying water creatures frightened out of hiding by the big turtle's violent passage through tangles of water weeds.

It was a nice arrangement while it lasted, but after a while the turtle moved off to deeper water, leaving the egret to his own devices.

Loons, Mergansers, and Others

OF ALL the occasional visitors to the pond, the hooded mergansers are probably the wildest in appearance. One morning five of them, two males and three females, idled about the middle of the pond for an hour or so just after daylight, then went on to wherever they were going.

As they posed and preened themselves, their outlines were softened by the thin blanket of early-morning mist that lay on the open water. A male, striking enough with his thin, spiky bill, brilliant yellow eye, and black head and neck, suddenly raised his crest, exposing the showy black-bordered white patch at his nape. The crests of the females by contrast were a soft, rosy gray-violet, a surprisingly handsome but ladylike accent to their otherwise sober gray-brown outfits.

Both the lone coot and the pied-billed grebe appeared to be fascinated by these exotic visitors. Leaving their lonely feeding places in the upper arm of the pond they joined the newcomers, following them about at a respectful distance for as long as they were in the neighborhood.

Later the wind came up, stirring small waves on the surface of the pond. Now and again a gust would catch a merganser's crest and tip it forward, giving the bird a surprisingly raffish appearance. Or it would blow another's tail straight up like a ruddy duck's, and the bird would suddenly skitter forward a few yards under full sail, to the apparent surprise of the more sedate coot and grebe.

The loons, coming on a day of windy spitting rain, brought a different sort of wildness to the pond. Great dark birds with neat all-over patterns of small white spots, they gave an impression of terrific vitality.

This was probably little more than a recreation stop, and most of their short stay was spent taking off one after the other from the water, circling the rim of the woods before landing again in great

plumes of spray. Occasionally the leader, feinting at
a landing, bumbled along just above the surface until
the others had lost flying speed, then with a few
strong wing strokes he flew upward again to repeat
his circling. The others, already on the water, saw
themselves tricked and there was a great hullabaloo,
for the loon cannot leap directly from the water but
must first make a long, pattering run on the surface
before he can become airborne.

So by the time they managed to get into the air
again, the leader would already be swinging around
into the wind for another landing. The wild game
was played at irregular intervals all morning, with
the leader of the movement sometimes successful in
tricking his followers, and sometimes not. Possibly
these were young birds combining strenuous play
with practice in the important business of quick
take-off and landing. The young wood ducks
occasionally do much the same thing.

The Wood Duck and the Turtle

EXCEPT for the hunters and their possible victims, the inhabitants of the wildlife preserve pay surprisingly little attention to one another when their paths cross in the course of the day's business. The big heron wading in the shallows steps over the muskrat feeding on a grass hummock without any comment being made by either. And the cottontail idling the day away in her grass form ignores the rustlings of the hunting lizard.

But the tempers of individuals vary, and now and again someone does take an unneighborly attitude toward a visitor. One morning two nearly-grown wood ducks were busy in the pond, paying no attention to the occasional soft warm showers. For an hour or more they zigzagged about in quick short rushes, stabbing at hurrying water bugs or ducking their heads below the surface to get at creatures clinging to the undersides of the floating lily pads. When their crops were full of this rich game they climbed out onto a short section of floating log to loaf and dress their feathers.

Two turtles were already in residence on the log, a huge black old slider and a smaller one a little larger than a saucer. Turtles sunning themselves seldom doze—they keep their necks stretched high

and a sharp eye on anything that moves in the neighborhood—so the ducks' appearance didn't take these two by surprise. They shifted positions a little as the extra weight upset the balance of the log, then returned to their business.

It was a small log, so with two turtles and two ducks on board, the space was somewhat crowded, but the large turtle seemed to take a philosophical view of the matter. The smaller one, however, looked at things differently. It may have been that the duck balancing on one foot beside him was keeping off some of the sunshine—or the turtle may simply have been one of those small individuals who always feel they are being imposed on by their larger neighbors.

At any rate he fidgeted and shifted his feet in petulant fashion each time the duck, stretching to smooth a hard-to-reach feather, rocked the log. Losing patience at last, he began reaching up to pinch at the duck's folded foot hanging so temptingly close overhead. The duck seemed not to take these gestures seriously; he'd peer down and make a half-friendly feint at the turtle's head with his beak and then go back to his preening.

This performance was repeated several times, with no apparent advantage to the turtle—until at last he flounced into the water and disappeared. The ducks and the old slider peacefully continued to share the log until the rain settled to a disagreeable drizzle. Then the old turtle went to the

bottom and the ducks, finding a sheltered place
under the bushes on the bank, put their heads under
their wings and settled down for a nap.

THE HUNTERS
AND THE HUNTED

The Hunters and the Hunted
Ants Pull Down a Caterpillar

The Hunters and the Hunted

VICIOUS life-and-death battles are constantly being fought in the weeds and thickets as one meat eater or another tries to make a meal of a neighbor. So one would expect the hunted to go about in constant terror of the hunters. But as a matter of fact they appear to take a surprisingly reasonable view of the whole thing. Naturally each creature takes considerable pains to avoid being the one to furnish a meal— but no one seems to brood too much over the matter.

A good many birds like to drink and bathe among the closely spaced stumps standing in the shallow water of the pond. One day, while the mourning dove was taking a drink from such a place she was spotted by the hawk. Warned by his shadow just before he struck, she sprang to one side losing only a single wing feather. For a moment or two they dodged this way and that, splashing the water and bumping into stumps—the hawk trying to regain his advantage and the dove frantically

77

trying to avoid his reaching talons. The hawk wasn't at his best in such a place, and the dove was able to escape through a space too small to allow the hawk's wide wings passage. Once she'd gotten well away into the open the hawk had no hope of catching her, so he settled on one of the snags while the dove went to the top of a nearby gum. The dove's reaction to this narrow escape seemed to be annoyance rather than terror. Muttering and complaining to herself, she dressed her ruffled feathers, ignoring the hawk who was philosophically dressing *his* ruffled feathers a hundred feet away.

Some time later she went off to finish her interrupted drink at another place, while the hawk caught a water snake and spent a half-hour or more in the high marsh grass tearing and hacking strips of tough meat off the slippery carcass.

In the little stagnant bush-shaded pool in the roadside ditch, the frogs and tadpoles react to the appearance of the banded water snake in much the same manner as the respectable citizens of a frontier town when the bad man, in a truculent humor, rides down the main street. There is a momentary flurry of activity, and small puffs of mud float like dust in the water as the inhabitants leave their watching places in the patches of weed and bury themselves in the muddy bottom.

If the snake has already fed, or if everybody has managed to find secure hiding places before he comes in sight, he may simply glide sinuously past,

just below the surface of the brown water, and disappear into the high weeds at the end of the pool. For a little while the place will continue to appear deserted. Then, one by one, the frogs will leave the mud to float as before, with just their bulging eyes and their nostrils showing above the brown scum. And the weeds and floating lily pads will again rock and heave from the periodic disturbances in the shadowy places below as tadpoles, minnows, and others go about the interrupted business of the day.

Of course the snake might take the trouble to search out some unfortunate's hiding place and make a meal of him. In that case the others—the lucky ones—would simply have stayed quiet in their own places, waiting for the dreadful business to be finished. And when he has finally gone elsewhere to digest his meal, there is a quiet time while everyone waits to see if the snake is planning on a second course. But in a surprisingly short time, everything considered, business is back to normal, with no gathering of neighbors to discuss the matter.

A peculiar small, crooning cry repeated at regular intervals from the thicket growing on the edge of the old dam sounded more like the complaint of a small bird than the voice of an animal. But after some search it proved to be coming from a field mouse being swallowed by the old black snake.

Tiny, sharply defined mouse tracks mixed with looping ropelike marks in the dusty path showed where the capture had been made. From there the snake had carried his victim to the closely matted flat top of the bush for the swallowing ceremony.

The black snake had draped his coils comfortably over the springy mat of leaves and by now had the mouse half swallowed, tail first. He went about his business in silence, as is the habit of serpents, alternately moving forward first his loosely hinged lower jaw a fraction of an inch and then the upper. It was a slow, deliberate process, but little by little the mouse was disappearing. And all the time he kept up his small conversation. It was no panic-stricken cry for help, but had more the tone of someone discussing the possibility of a small loan with his banker—or suggesting to the finance people that they come back another day for the television instead of taking it today.

A most peculiar performance, for the mouse kept up his gentle argument until he'd entirely disappeared. Then, after a few muffled afterthoughts he was silent. During the entire time he seemed not to feel that he'd been overtaken by a dreadful catastrophe, but simply that it had turned out to be one of those days when simply nothing goes right.

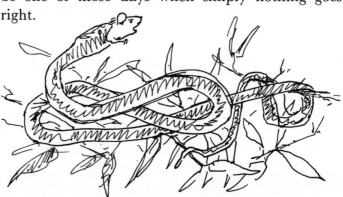

Other deadly battles are fought in complete silence by both sides. A tiny black wasp no more than a half-inch long made a fighting pass at a spider resting among the top leaves of a nearby bush. The fat yellow spider is five times her antagonist's weight, and a dangerous fighter in her own right. But the war between wasps and spiders is an old one, with the wasps often fighting far out of their class; and the ritual for such encounters is pretty well established.

If on her first pass the wasp is able to take the spider by surprise, the struggle will of course be over almost before it begins. But nobody here lives to fat old age who isn't continually alert. Besides, in order to paralyze her victim without killing her, the wasp must reach certain vulnerable nerve centers on the creature's underside, and that is difficult to do without coming in range of the spider's own poison fangs.

So, often as not, the wasp misses her first thrust, and the spider is given a chance for her life. In that situation most spiders simply fling themselves overboard and fall straight to the ground in hopes of hiding under the leaves there. But this particular spider had other ideas—perhaps she wasn't altogether convinced that such a tiny wasp could really be dangerous. At any rate, she leaped off the leaf, but instead of falling free she left her life line attached to the leaf and let herself down by reeling it out behind her. And that turned out to be a fatal mistake.

As she swung and turned, defenseless at the end
of the slowly lengthening line, the wasp returned to
the attack. Circling and swooping she struck time
after time at the spider's exposed underside, so that
by the time the spider came to rest halfway down
a steep sandy bank she was already partially
paralyzed. Lighting beside her the wasp quickly
examined the now helpless spider and carefully
injected a last bit of venom before going a short way
off to polish and clean herself.

When she came back she looked her prize over
again, then set about the business of getting it up
off the ground where it would be safe from the ants.
She still had to dig a nursery burrow and she
didn't want anything to happen to the meat while
she was gone.

Taking a firm grip of one of the spider's pedi-
palpi, she started backing up the bank. It seemed
unlikely that she would be able to move such a big
load, but with much slipping and sliding she did.
Backing out onto a slope of loose scree she started
a small avalanche that carried her a couple of
inches downhill before she was able to get onto
firmer ground once more. But before long she had
reached the foot of the six-inch perpendicular cliff.
The footing there was firmer, and after taking a
new grip on her burden, she started backing
briskly up the sheer face with the big spider swinging freely from her jaws. But getting such an
awkward bundle over the lip of the little cliff and
onto the slope above proved difficult. Backing up

over the edge she braced herself for the final effort needed to swing the load up and over. But she lost her footing on the loose sand and fell again to the bottom.

With spiders as plentiful as they are, it seemed foolish to go to so much trouble trying to get this one out of such a difficult situation. But the wasp is a stubborn creature and once she starts a project it seldom occurs to her to give it up. After four more failures she finally managed to drag her spider all the way to the top of the bank and wedge it among the roots of the bushes there.

But she still wasn't satisfied—before she went off to dig the burrow she wanted her prize safely hung up off the ground. So as soon as she had rested a little and cleaned the worst of the dust off herself, she took another grip on the creature and started backing up one of the bushes.

It was a nerve-racking business to watch— the spider's dangling legs would catch on things so that only by dint of much jerking and shaking was the wasp able to get them free. Or, not being able to see behind her, she'd take a wrong turning at a fork, back out onto a twig or leaf that led no-where, and laboriously have to retrace her steps.

A limp, paralyzed spider is an awkward thing to hang securely, and when she did at last put this one down in what she considered a suitable place it simply slid away and fell to the ground again.

The tiny wasp repeated the entire performance at least three times before she succeeded at last in hooking the spider's legs securely over the edge of a leaf a foot above the ground. With that done, she rested and groomed herself for a few minutes before dropping down to begin a burrow in the sand close by.

The digging took three quarters of an hour, and during that time the wasp made a dozen trips up into the leaves to make sure the spider was undisturbed. When all was ready at last, she dropped the creature unceremoniously to the ground, dragged it to the hole she'd dug, and after one more quick inspection took it inside. When she had attached a single egg firmly to the underside of the still living spider, she refilled the gallery with dirt, scattering the excess to hide all signs of her recent digging. Then, after circling the place a time or two, she flew off.

When the egg hatched, the young one would feed on the fresh meat provided by the paralyzed spider—and later on would dig its way to the surface to begin life with no help from anybody.

Ants Pull Down a Caterpillar

THE HAIRY white caterpillar unhurriedly crossing the small sun-baked clearing paid no attention when the first small black ants, advance scouts of a scattered hunting pack, began to trail him. And it did seem improbable that they could be any serious threat to a creature so much larger and stronger than they.

However, the small black ants are fierce wolfish creatures, and here was meat on the hoof. So while the caterpillar rippled placidly along they ran excited exploratory circles around him. But no matter where they attacked, along his sides or on his back, they found that the caterpillar's long, close-growing bristly hairs effectively protected his soft body from their bites. And when an ant more reckless than the rest did manage to work his way under the bristles brushing the ground at the caterpillar's sides, he found himself unceremoniously booted out by one of the creature's many feet before he could damage the soft underside.

But in spite of the discouraging prospect, ants continued to swarm in from all sides, dropping whatever they happened to be doing to join in the attempt to pull the caterpillar down. Before long they were gathered around him like wolves about a straggler from a buffalo herd. Some ran backward and forward alongside in seemingly aimless patterns, while others climbed over the bristling tips of the hairs that protected the creature's back.

Meanwhile the caterpillar still trudged placidly on his way, and it wasn't until he was nearly half-way across the clearing that the ants' activity began to show results. Then, little by little, the caterpillar's appearance began to change. He seemed to be growing smaller. And his fine furry coat had taken on a ragged, moth-eaten look.

The ants hadn't been wasting their time after all—as they climbed about over the caterpillar they'd been giving him a haircut. Using their sharp mandibles as barber scissors, they snipped away at the troublesome bristles, shortening them bit by bit until one after another of the hunters was able to reach past the remaining stubs to the tender skin beneath.

At the first such bite the caterpillar flinched but kept steadily on his way, and it wasn't until he was suddenly stung in a dozen different places that he seemed to realize he was in trouble. Then, rearing and twisting his head over his back, he managed to dislodge some of his tormentors, but as fast as one was brushed away another took his place. The shearing, also, was going faster now, so that more and more of his body was exposed to attack.

As he flung himself about trying to fight off the enemies on his back, dozens more rushed to attack his exposed underside.

Even then the fight was not over by any means, but little by little the caterpillar weakened and before long a line of bearers carrying bits of caterpillar meat formed a living black thread winding from the location of the butchering place to the burrow at the edge of the clearing.

At sundown the bloody work was still going on— and next morning all trace of the butchering had been cleared away. Wolves could not have done any better.

FALL RAINS
AND WINTER QUARTERS

Fall Rains and Winter Quarters

THE END of summer brings many changes to the old mill pond and the thickets around the little clearing. But the greatest recommendation for these small informal wildlife preserves is that they are open for business at all times and in all sorts of weather. Early or late, rain or shine, there is always some small thing to be seen if only one learns how and where to look.

A hurricane turning inland brought with it the heaviest rainfall in years, and by the time the storm was over every stream in the area was running bankfull, and the level of the old mill pond had risen nearly three feet.

At the edge of the clearing a family of flying squirrels, dispossessed when their nest tree was blown down, clung tightly to the gray bark of a slender blackjack. Being night workers they were waiting for dusk—refusing to move in daylight even while my canoe was being unloaded and launched a few feet away.

At the head of the pond wind and rushing water
had uprooted trees, blocking many of the winding
swamp channels, and masses of driftwood and trash
floated in the backwaters, making progress difficult.
Snakes driven from their hiding places by the rising
water had taken refuge in the tops of bushes, almost
ignored by the birds who were already coming out
of the juniper thickets and smilax tangles where
they'd waited out the storm.

What at first appeared to be a life-size gray-and-
white toy duck caught in the shadows under a
bundle of floating brush turned out to be a sleeping
coot. Wakened by a touch of the canoe paddle, he
suddenly came to life with a startled squawk and
pattered away over the water in his peculiar take-
off run before flapping heavily into the air.

At the edge of the gum thickets the beaver lodge,
a mound of sticks and mud several feet high, was
almost entirely underwater. The sleeping and living chambers deep inside, usually a couple of feet
above water level, were now completely flooded and
the two half-grown kits huddled on the very top of
the tiny island of tangled sticks. Apparently the old
one had placed the kits there with instructions not
to move—as a doe does when she hides her fawn.
They quietly watched the boat but made no move
of any kind.

While we watched each other, the old muskrat who owned a burrow at the base of the beaver lodge came swimming out of a tangle of floating briars and crawled onto the little island. Clambering cautiously toward the young beavers, she poked her head into the tangle of sticks beneath their feet. A movement of drab gray fur in the shadows turned out to be the muskrat's kittens, who had also been put there for safety.

After inspecting her young ones, the muskrat turned to go and met the old beaver who was just coming out of the water, but made no sign of recognition. The beaver sat for a moment or two with her tail floating on the water, nearsightedly peering at her kits, then turned and swam away as the old muskrat had done.

The old beaver had made no sound as she sat there, but apparently there was some communication between her and the kits. She had no more than turned away than they scrambled from their perch and plunged into the water like children being let out of school. At first they simply swam quietly about, seemingly fascinated by the unfamiliar appearance of the swirling flood water. Later a game of tag played with drifting sticks and leaves was interrupted by the appearance of a marsh rabbit, who unconcernedly climbed onto the lodge top to shake the water out of his wet fur and scratch for a flea before swimming off into the shadows. A swimming snake on his way to higher ground was followed at a respectful distance by the kits. But before they'd gone far they caught the busy scraping sounds of the

old beaver peeling a green stick for her supper and swam off through the flooded thickets to join her.

The next day the falling water exposed a temporary den, where the old beaver and the kits had spent the night, under the roots of a big sycamore standing just in the edge of the flood. To them the high water was an inconvenience, but nothing more.

On sunny days between frosty nights or cold rains there is a constant rattling and stirring under the loose blanket of newly fallen leaves as snakes, beetles, lizards, and others who dislike cold weather search for snug winter quarters. Piles of half-rotted last years' leaves, hollow logs, and rotted stumps are in great demand, and a careful search of such places will turn up all manner of curious tenants.

This is the time of year when bright spots of new wood appear on the dead snags around the pond where gray squirrels and flickers are enlarging the entrances of abandoned nest holes they'll use for shelter from the cold rains. Ragged strings of moss or fine grass hanging from other smaller doorways show where flying squirrels are packing bedding into their winter quarters.

There Is No End to the Small Mysteries

NO MATTER how closely one watches these small wildlife preserves there never seems to be an end to the surprises. Now, while the others are looking for winter quarters, a new kind of wasp appears, digging brood burrows in the hard clay of the road. But before it is possible to learn anything of her habits, frost comes and she disappears as mysteriously as she appears. So there is nothing to do but make a note of the date and circumstances, and wait for her appearance next year.

For three consecutive years a single large black wasp, with thread waist and neat brown markings on her legs, has appeared during the last warm fall days. Selecting an abandoned carpenter bee burrow in one of the dead trees at the edge of the clearing, she starts carrying grass into it. Snipping a bit of stem or blade anywhere from two to six inches long, she takes a tight grip of one end with her jaws and flies back with the timber dangling awkwardly below her.

The limber grass blades give her little trouble as she drags them inside, but the stems are another matter. Just inside the entrance these old carpenter bee tunnels make a right-angle turn, and the stiffer bits are hard to drag around the bend. If one slips out of her grasp in the process the wasp makes no effort to recover it but simply flies off for a new one. So as she works, a steadily growing accumulation of discarded material litters the ground below, marking the progress of her work.

Sometimes she gets one end of a stem wedged inside the hole while the other still sticks out in the open. Buzzing and muttering to herself she tries to remedy the matter by looping the piece so that both ends can be dragged inside together, but often enough she succeeds only in pulling the whole thing out.

It is a most peculiar performance, but each year before I can discover how she builds a nest of such material, and what sort of food she supplies for her young ones, a woodpecker has drilled the tunnel out, destroying all the evidence. All that is ever left are bits of a tightly curled cylinder of grass and bits of what look like old cushion stuffing.

Perhaps next year I'll be able to find out just what she does.

A single tightly crumpled leaf hanging from an otherwise bare twig turns out to have been fastened to the branch and drawn into its curious shape by a lacing of almost invisible threads. And inside, safe from the prying eyes of birds, a tiny jumping spider drowses away the cold rainy days in a soft, dry gossamer sleeping chamber. It would be good to know more about how he does these things.

Breaking open an old stump and finding that a

toad, lizard, or snake has made his winter quarters deep inside the soft mass of rotting wood is a reminder to pay more attention to such places next summer.

So, no matter how small a piece of ground may be, there is always some sort of wild game to be found there. Small game, true. But from a few inches away a hunting beetle is no smaller than the charging rhinoceros on the television screen . . . and to his neighbors he's just as dangerous. It all depends on the point of view.

About the Author

GLEN ROUNDS has been at home with nature and wildlife ever since his boyhood on a horse ranch in the Powder River Country of Montana. After high school he worked in road and lumber camps and sawmills, and later turned to sign painting, lightning portraits, etching, engraving, and finally painting. He wandered throughout most of the United States watching people and animals, drawing what pleased him, and in 1935 accidentally started writing stories to go with his illustrations. *Ol' Paul, the Mighty Logger* (1936) was his first book; since then he has had almost thirty books published, most recently *Beaver Business* and *Wild Orphan,* and has illustrated for many other writers.

Mr. Rounds lives with his wife and son in Southern Pines, North Carolina.

Date Due